GrueSome AND GROSS

Sticker and Activity Fun

Animals

igloobooks

PIECES OF PREY

The shrike uses its sharp beak to cut its prey into pieces.
Match these halves together to form the four unfortunate victims.

A   B   C   E   F   G   D   H

PESKY PIGEONS

These naughty pigeons can't help pooing as they fly. Follow the lines to
find out which of the pigeons is responsible for each pooey mess.

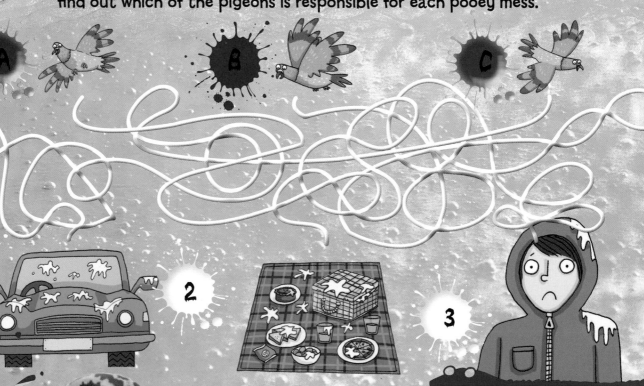

A   B   C

1   2   3

ANSWERS ON PAGE 16

2

UGLY CLOSE-UP

This unusual-looking axolotl lives in the darkest depths of the sea.
Which of the splat close-ups is not from this picture?

A

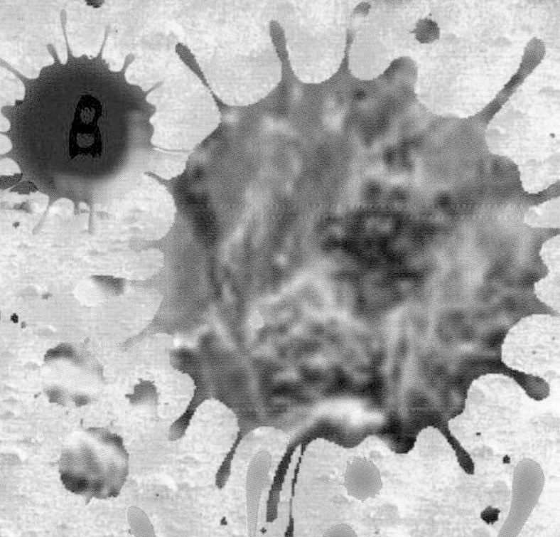

B

C

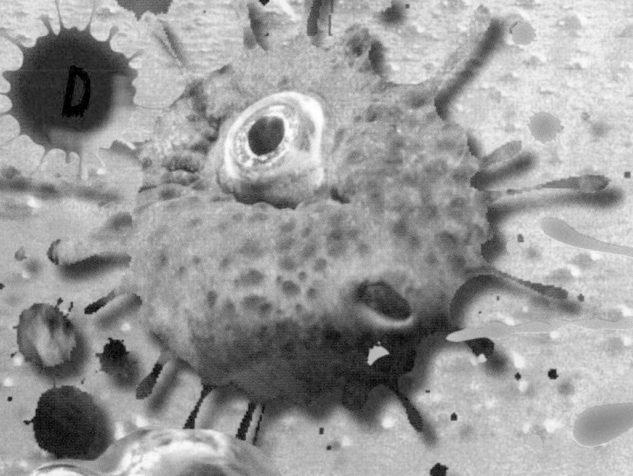

D

E

GROSS FACT

Axolotls can regrow
arms and legs that have
been cut off.

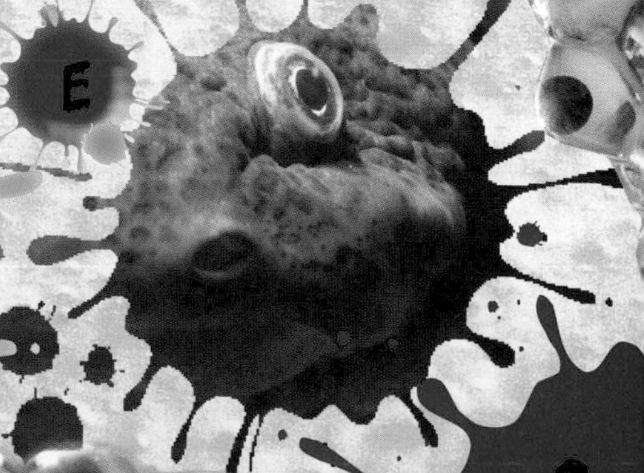

COWPAT BINGO

The cows have passed through the field and left a few messy deposits along the way.
Which of the bingo cards match the pattern of the cowpats on the field?

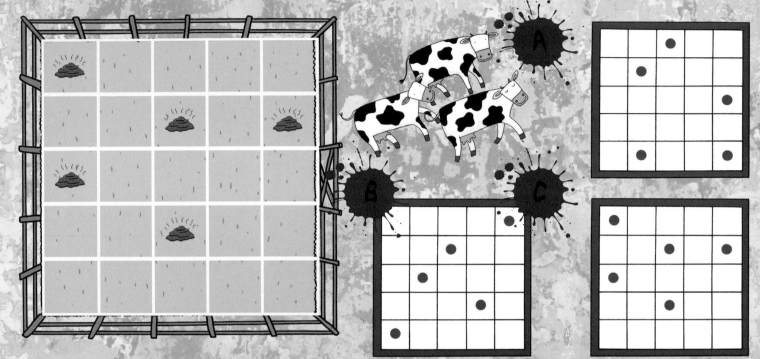

FUNNY FROGS

This swarm of slimy frogs are all jumbled up.

Draw a line between the matching frogs to form a pair.

CHAMELEON COPY GRID

Use the gridlines in the picture to help you copy
this scaly chameleon into the grid below.

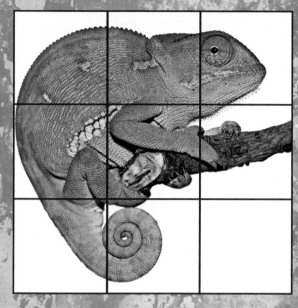

COOL FACT

Chameleons have the
ability to change skin
colour to match
their surroundings

ROADKILL MATCH

These unfortunate animals have been squished by a passing car.
Match each of the animals to the correct splat.

A B C D

1 2 3 4

JOIN THE DOTS

Join the dots and find out which filthy animal is creating a stink,
then decorate the scene with your best pens and pencils.

ANSWERS ON PAGE 16

ROTTING MEAT MAZE

This giant petrel feeds on the meat of dead animals. Help this one to reach its meal by drawing a line through the maze to the rotting meat.

START

FINISH

PIRANHA-INFESTED WATERS

John and James have stumbled upon a piranha-infested river whilst exploring the jungle, and the only way out is to wade through it. Who will make it out of the dangerous river first?

GAME RULES

1) You will need a friend and a dice to play this game. Each player should find a sticker on their sticker sheet and attach it to a coin to use as a counter. Place the counters on the START space.

2) Players take it in turns to roll the dice and move their counter the correct number of spaces around the board. If a player lands on an action square, then they should follow the instructions and move their counter accordingly.

3) The winner of the game is the first person to get through the perilous river and reach the FINISH.

START

1

2

3

4

A cow falls into the river. That will keep the piranhas busy. Roll again.

18

19

20

21

You slip off a stone and a piranha narrowly misses biting your toes. Miss a go.

SKUNK

GRUESOME RATING: 5

GROSS RATING: 7

SMELL FACTOR: 6

SPECIAL RATING:
POTENT STINK: 6

PIRANHA

GRUESOME RATING: 7

GROSS RATING: 2

SMELL FACTOR: 1

SPECIAL RATING:
BLOODTHIRSTY: 8

TURKEY VULTURE

GRUESOME RATING: 3

GROSS RATING: 7

SMELL FACTOR: 2

SPECIAL RATING:
PROJECTILE VOMIT: 8

HAGFISH

GRUESOME RATING: 4

GROSS RATING: 8

SMELL FACTOR: 5

SPECIAL RATING:
FLEXIBILITY: 5

PIG

GRUESOME RATING: 5

GROSS RATING: 7

SMELL FACTOR: 6

SPECIAL RATING:
FILTH DWELLING: 8

MOUSE

GRUESOME RATING: 1

GROSS RATING: 5

SMELL FACTOR: 5

SPECIAL RATING:
CHEESE FIEND: 4

HIPPO

GRUESOME RATING: 4

GROSS RATING: 4

SMELL FACTOR: 7

SPECIAL RATING:
MUD WALLOWING: 5

FROG

GRUESOME RATING: 3

GROSS RATING: 6

SMELL FACTOR: 4

SPECIAL RATING:
SLIMINESS: 7

BATTLE CARDS

HOW TO PLAY:

1. Press out the playing cards, shuffle the deck and divide the cards between each player. Each player must hold their cards face up in a pile and look only at the top card.

2. The first player should read out a category from their card and the corresponding score (e.g. Smell Factor 7). The second player then reads out the score for the same category from their top card.

3. The player with the highest score wins and gets to take the other player's card. Both of the cards from that round should be placed at the bottom of the winner's deck.

PIRANHA-INFESTED WATERS –
PAGE 8-9

SLIMY SUDOKU – PAGE 10

LLAMA

GRUESOME RATING: 1

GROSS RATING: 6

SMELL FACTOR: 4

SPECIAL RATING:
SPIT SHOT: 7

PIGEON

GRUESOME RATING: 2

GROSS RATING: 6

SMELL FACTOR: 3

SPECIAL RATING:
FLYING MENACE: 6

HOOPOE

GRUESOME RATING: 2

GROSS RATING: 6

SMELL FACTOR: 5

SPECIAL RATING:
POO SHOOTING: 8

SHRIKE

GRUESOME RATING: 7

GROSS RATING: 4

SMELL FACTOR: 2

SPECIAL RATING:
DICING PREY: 7

RABBIT

GRUESOME RATING: 2

GROSS RATING: 6

SMELL FACTOR: 4

SPECIAL RATING:
PELLET POOING: 5

COW

GRUESOME RATING: 2

GROSS RATING: 7

SMELL FACTOR: 6

SPECIAL RATING:
REGURGITATION 6

HORSE

GRUESOME RATING: 2

GROSS RATING: 5

SMELL FACTOR: 7

SPECIAL RATING:
SPEEDY RUNNER: 7

SHARK

GRUESOME RATING: 8

GROSS RATING: 3

SMELL FACTOR: 2

SPECIAL RATING:
BLOOD HUNTER: 4

4. The winner of each round gets to choose a category from their next card.

5. If both players read out an equal value, they must read out their special category and corresponding score as a tie-breaker. Whichever player has the highest score wins the round and takes the cards. If the special category scores are equal, then the cards should be placed into a pile between the two players. The next player to win a round collects the pile, as well as the other player's card.

6. The winner of the game is the player with all of the cards at the end of the game.

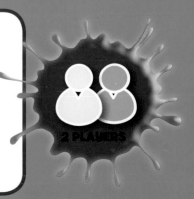
2 PLAYERS

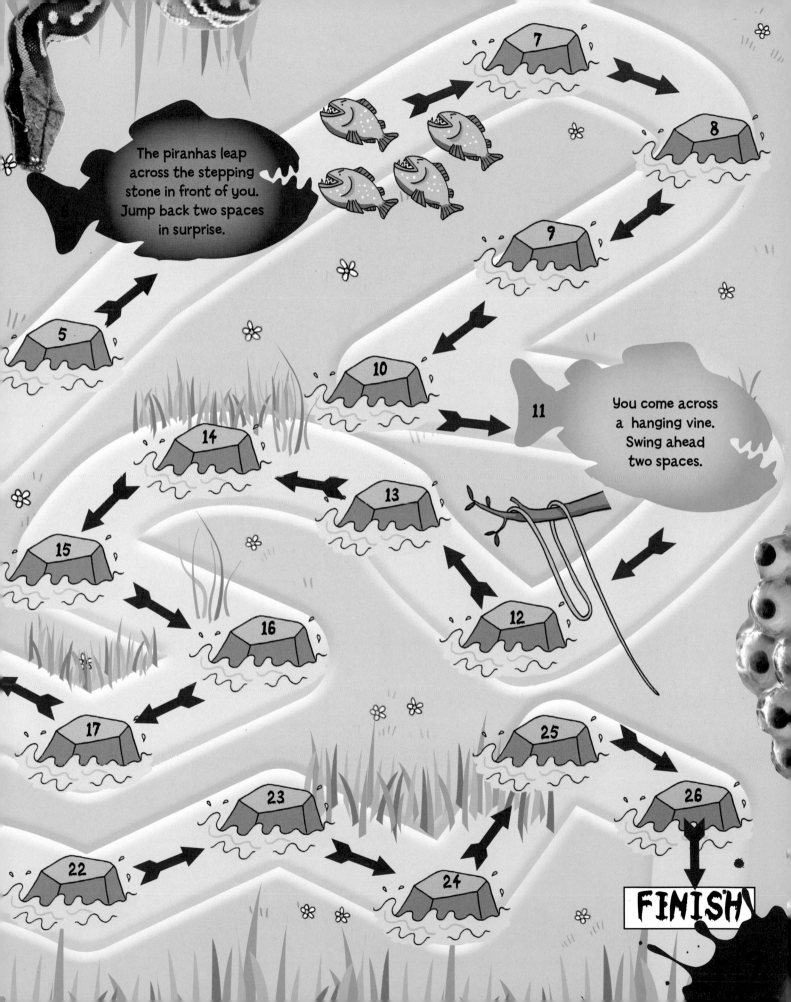

SURINAM TOAD MEMORY TEST

The surinam toad embeds her eggs in her back and carries the spawn until they burst out of the skin as tadpoles. Look at this scene for 30 seconds and answer the questions on page 12.

SLIMY SUDOKU

Use the stickers from your sticker sheet to complete this grid of ugly aquatic creatures so that there is only one of each animal in any row, or column.

10

ANSWERS ON PAGE 16

MUCKY MOLE

The star-nosed mole has a strange nose that looks like an open flower.
Use your best pens and pencils to decorate this picture.

COOL FACT

The star-nosed mole
uses the tentacles
around its nose to
feel its way around.

MEMORY TEST QUESTIONS

1) The fish swimming behind the toad are red, yellow and...?

2) How many frogspawn are embedded in the toad's back?

3) Which direction is the red fish pointing – left or right?

4) How many tadpoles are swimming above the toad?

HORSE MANURE TRAIL PUZZLE

Guide this horse around the field, by drawing only in straight lines and without drawing diagonally, so that the horse can cover every square of the field with manure.

KOMODO DRAGON JIGSAW

The Komodo dragon has a vile, bacteria-infected mouth that it uses to kill big animals. Match the jigsaw pieces to the gaps to complete the picture.

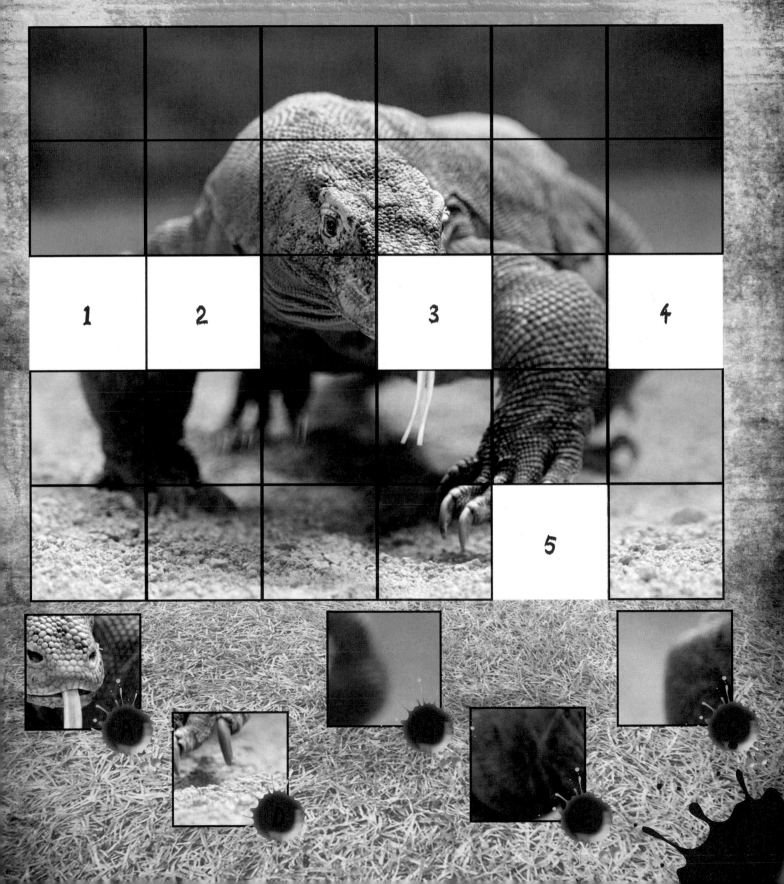

COWPAT MINI MAZE

This cow has been greedily grazing in the field and there's only one place for the grass to go. Draw a line through the cow's intestines to digest the grass and turn it into a cowpat.

VOMITING VULTURE

The turkey vulture vomits on animals before it eats them. Draw a line between each animal and its vomit-covered double to make a pair.

A

B

C

D

1

2

3

4

ANSWERS ON PAGE 16

HORRIBLE ANIMAL FACTS

Work your way through this list of weird animal facts
and decide whether each fact is true, or false.

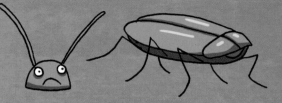

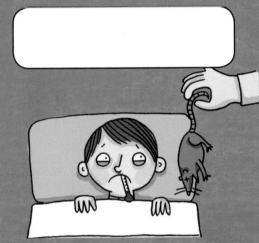

1) A cockroach can survive without its head for nine days, at which point it dies from starvation.

2) The roadrunner bird eats its young if they don't grow fast enough.

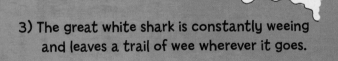

3) The great white shark is constantly weeing and leaves a trail of wee wherever it goes.

4) In Bolivia, the blood of rats has been used as a cure for the common cold for over a hundred years.

5) The hagfish excretes a slimy gel to escape predators and rinses it off by tying itself in a knot.

6) The hoopoe shoots poo in the eyes of its predators.

ANSWER PAGE

Page 2
PIECES OF PREY: A-G, B-E, C-F, D-H
PESKY PIGEONS: A-2, B-3, C-1

Page 3
UGLY CLOSE-UP:
The odd one out is B

Page 4
COWPAT BINGO: Card C
FUNNY FROGS: A-F, B-H, C-J, D-I, E-G

Page 6
ROADKILL MATCH:
A-3, B-4, C-1, D-2

Page 7
CARRION MAZE:

Page 10
SLIMY SUDOKU:

Page 12
MEMORY TEST QUESTIONS:
1) Blue
2) 22
3) Left
4) Three

HORSE MANURE TRAIL PUZZLE:

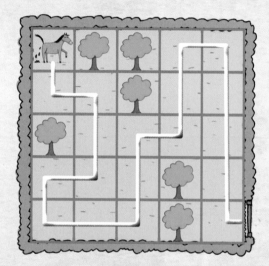

Page 13
KOMODO DRAGON JIGSAW: 1-C, 2-E, 3-A, 4-B, 5-D

Page 14
COWPAT MINI MAZE:

VOMITING VULTURE: A-3, B-4, C-1, D-2

Page 15
HORRIBLE ANIMAL FACTS:
1)True 2) True 3) False 4) False 5) True 6) True